SCRABBLE

BRAND Crossword Game

Junior

Superspelling
Games

My name is _____ .

I am _____ years old.

I go to _____ School.

I am _____
at spelling!

James David

Collins

THE ALPHABET

There are 26 letters in the alphabet.
Each of these pictures starts with a different letter.
Say the words and fill in the letters.

These letters of the alphabet are in the right order, but some are missing. Fill the gaps.

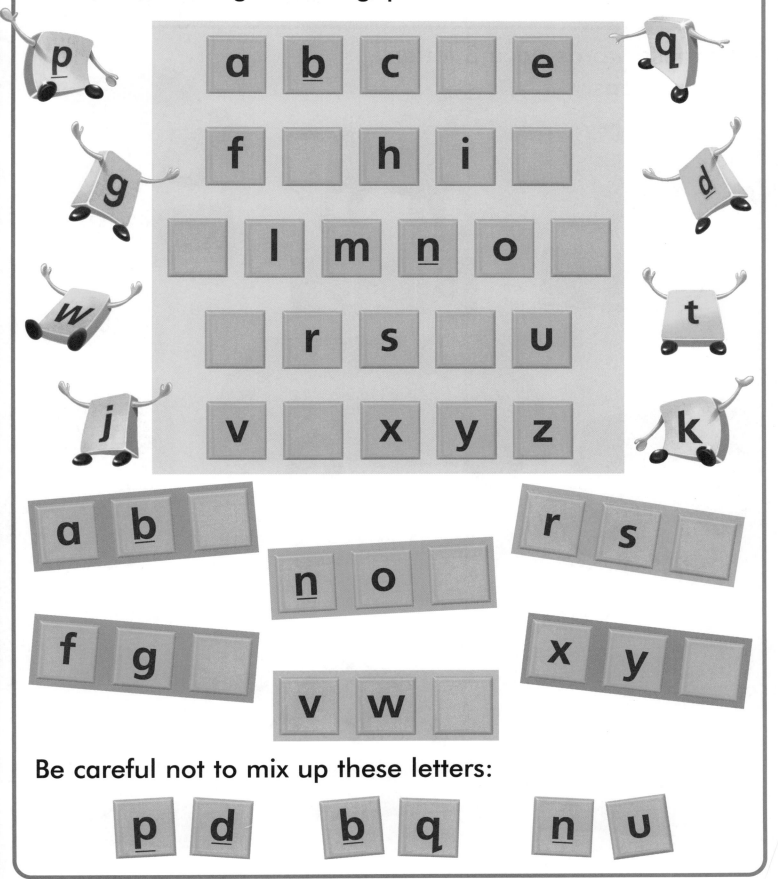

Be careful not to mix up these letters:

p   d   b   q   n   u

All these words have 3 letters.
Fill the gaps.

c _ _

d _ _

_ _ r

_ _ n

_ u _

_ e _

_ _ t

_ o _

_ _ n

Crossword

Fill the gaps in these 3-letter words to make a crossword. Look at the pictures for clues!

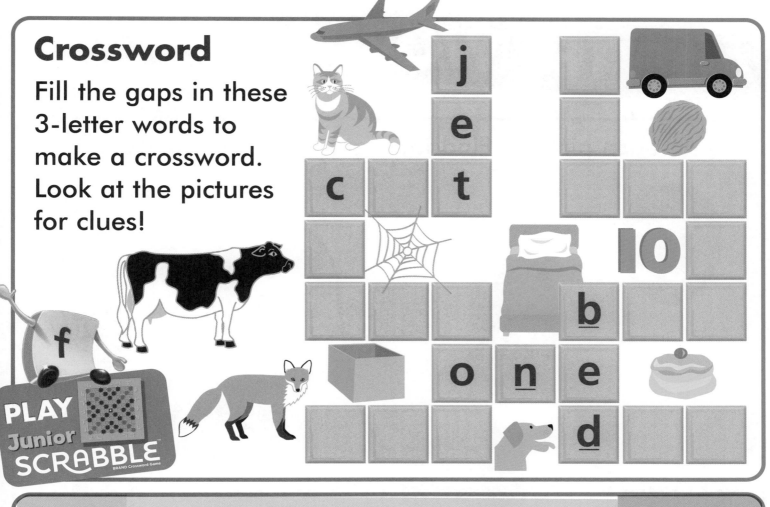

Find the word

What can you see in this kitchen? Write in all the 3-letter words.

tap
cup
mug
bin
jug
pan

4-LETTER WORDS

Name each picture. Find the right word. Fill the gaps.

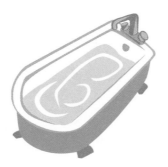
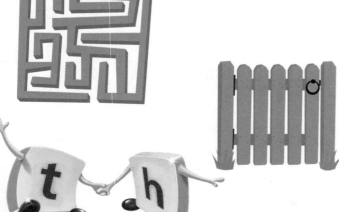

c a _ _

g a _ _

m a _ _

s a _ _

b a _ _

f a _ _

p a _ _

I-spy

Name each picture. Find the right word. Fill the gaps.

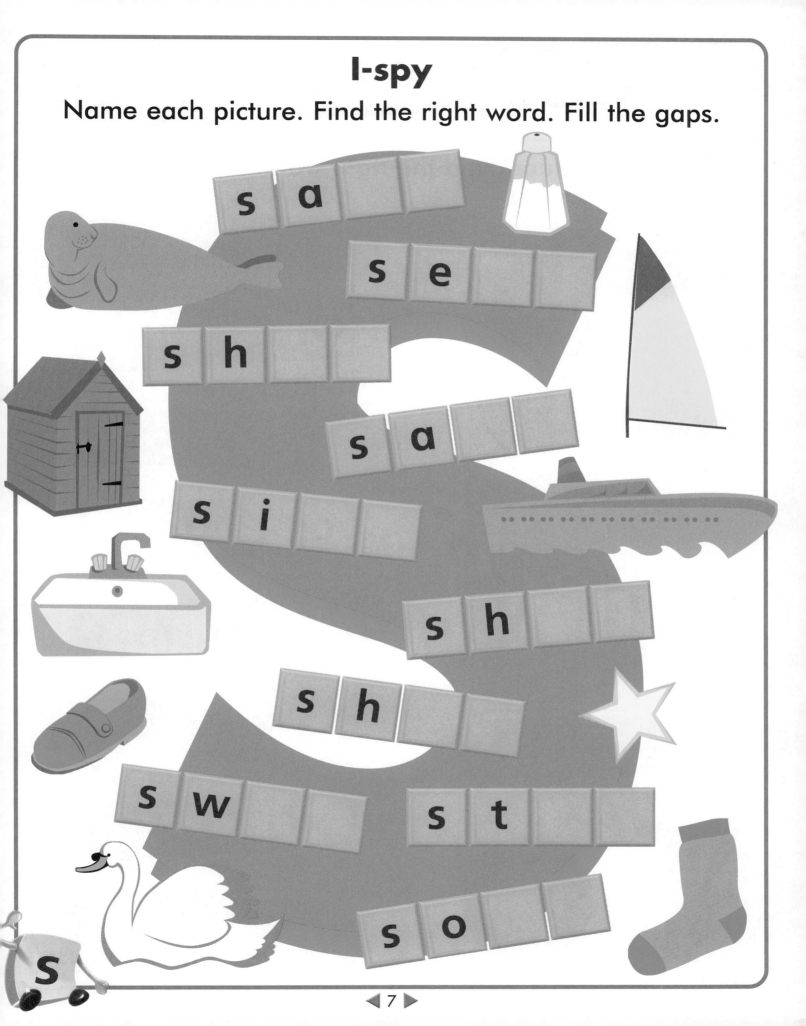

Name each picture. Find the right word. Fill the gaps.

t	a	b		

w	h			l

		o	o	n

c	l	o		

		a	n	t

b	r	u		

t	r			n

| | | a | | l | e |

◀ 8 ▶

Missing letters

Fill the gaps to make a 5-letter word for each picture.

p l _ _ e

h a _ _ y

s h _ _ p

_ _ a d e

c r _ _ e

c l _ _ d

c l _ _ n

_ _ a l e

c a r

What kind of transport do you like best?
Fill in all the names.

Crossword

Use the same words to make this crossword.

Word search

Can you find all the words?

car (crossed out)
bus
van
bike
ship
lorry
plane

s	h	i	p	b	x	t	r	a	i	n
t	f	b	l	z	c	a	r	l	j	c
a	t	u	a	v	a	n	b	o	k	o
x	r	s	n	m	t	k	i	r	m	a
i	s	l	e	d	g	e	k	r	q	c
s	c	o	o	t	e	r	e	y	s	h

taxi
coach
sledge
tanker
scooter
train

◄ 11 ►

HEADS AND TAILS

Fill the middle squares with letters that will end the first word, and start the second word.

b e [ ] o g

s i [ ] e a

t o [ ] e t

h a [ ] w o

c o [ ] e b

a r [ ] u g

Do the same for these 4-letter words.

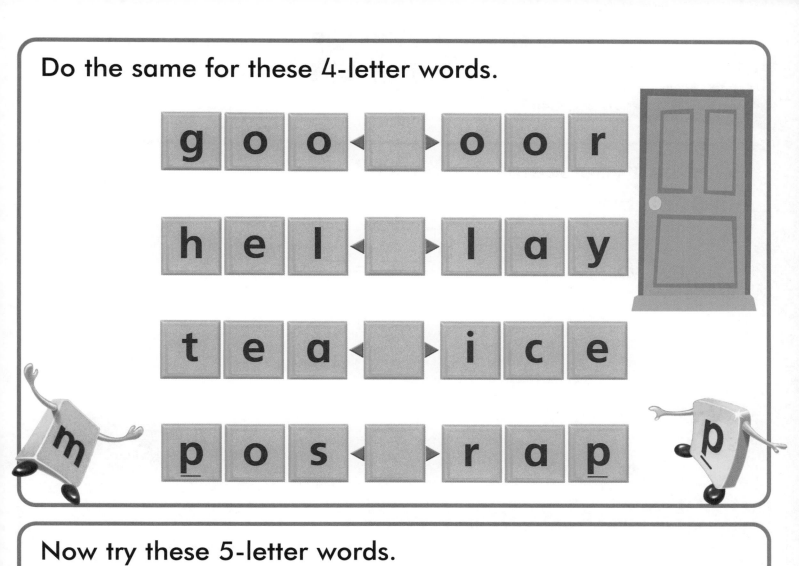

g o o ◄ ► o o r

h e l ◄ ► l a y

t e a ◄ ► i c e

p o s ◄ ► r a p

Now try these 5-letter words.

d r e a ◄ ► e t a l

t o o t ◄ ► o u n d

t a b l ◄ ► a r l y

d r e s ◄ ► h o u t

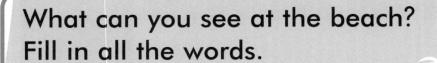

AT THE SEASIDE

What can you see at the beach?
Fill in all the words.

s____

b___d__

c__o____

s___

s_____

s__i___

s____

w__v___

f_____

r_____

b____h

p_____

c_____

s___d_

s_____

sh_____

Crossword

Use the same words to make this crossword.

PLAY
Junior
SCRABBLE
BRAND Crossword Game

JUMBLE WORDS

Join each jumbled word on the left to its picture. Then join each picture to the start of its word on the right, and fill the gaps.

 e j t

 y e k

 o f x

 i e c

 n h e

 p u c

 e e y

 l g o

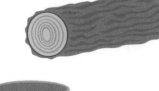

 f

 c

 k

 e

 j

 h

 l

 i

Do the same with these 4-letter words.

m d u r

k o o b

o c s k

b

s

d

Now try these 5-letter words.

m u e o s

l c o k c

p a s t m

c

s

m

IN THE TOY SHOP

Join each jumbled label to the right toy, and fill in the right spelling.

lodl

etki

pto

oatb

toorb

bta

enarc

wncol

tfro

knat

Crossword

Use the same words to make this crossword.

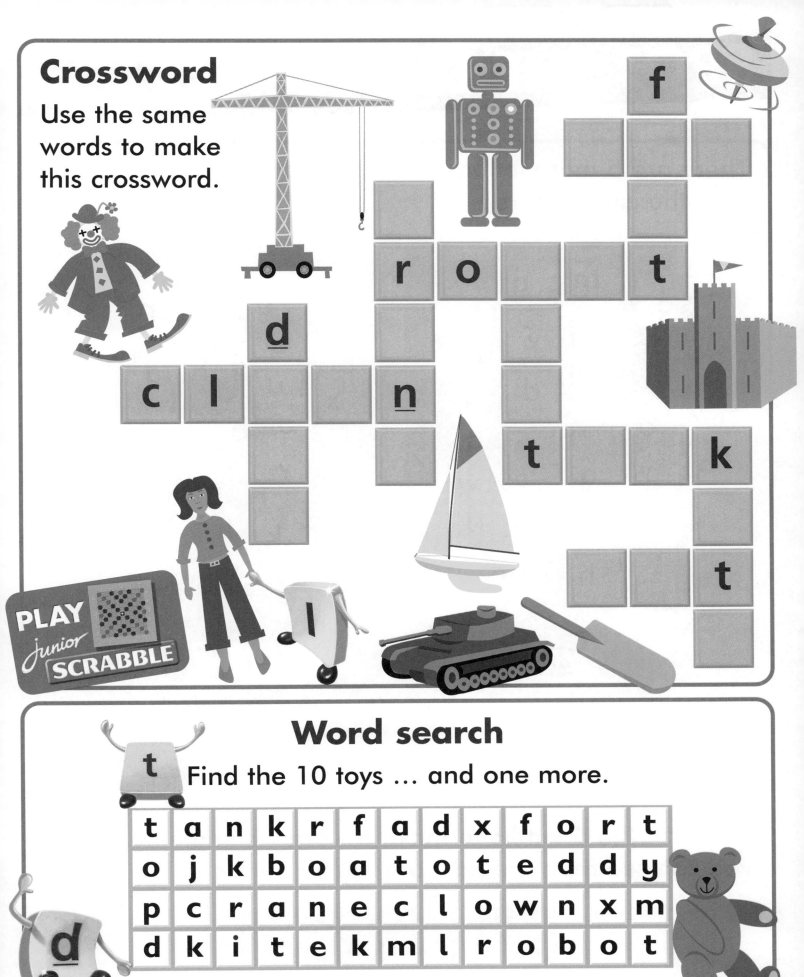

f

r o   t

d

c l   n

t   k

t

PLAY junior SCRABBLE

Word search

Find the 10 toys ... and one more.

t	a	n	k	r	f	a	d	x	f	o	r	t
o	j	k	b	o	a	t	o	t	e	d	d	y
p	c	r	a	n	e	c	l	o	w	n	x	m
d	k	i	t	e	k	m	l	r	o	b	o	t

There are 5 more letters in the second balloon.
Ring the extra letters.

Now use the 5 letters to make a word – something
you can see from the balloon!

Find the animals

Sort each set of 5 letters to make an animal.
Fill in the words in the rows below.

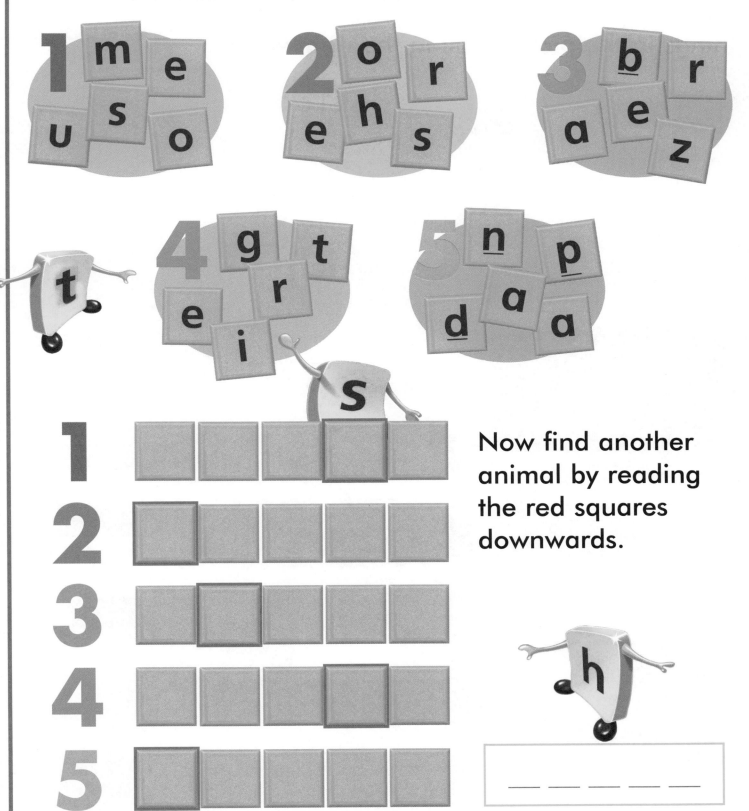

Now find another animal by reading the red squares downwards.

IN THE BEDROOM

c h

Match each jumbled word to one of the things in the picture. Fill in the right word.

lfesh

dbe

gur

klcoc

wodiwn

lbate

odro

hciar

teprac

Crossword

Use the same words to make this crossword.

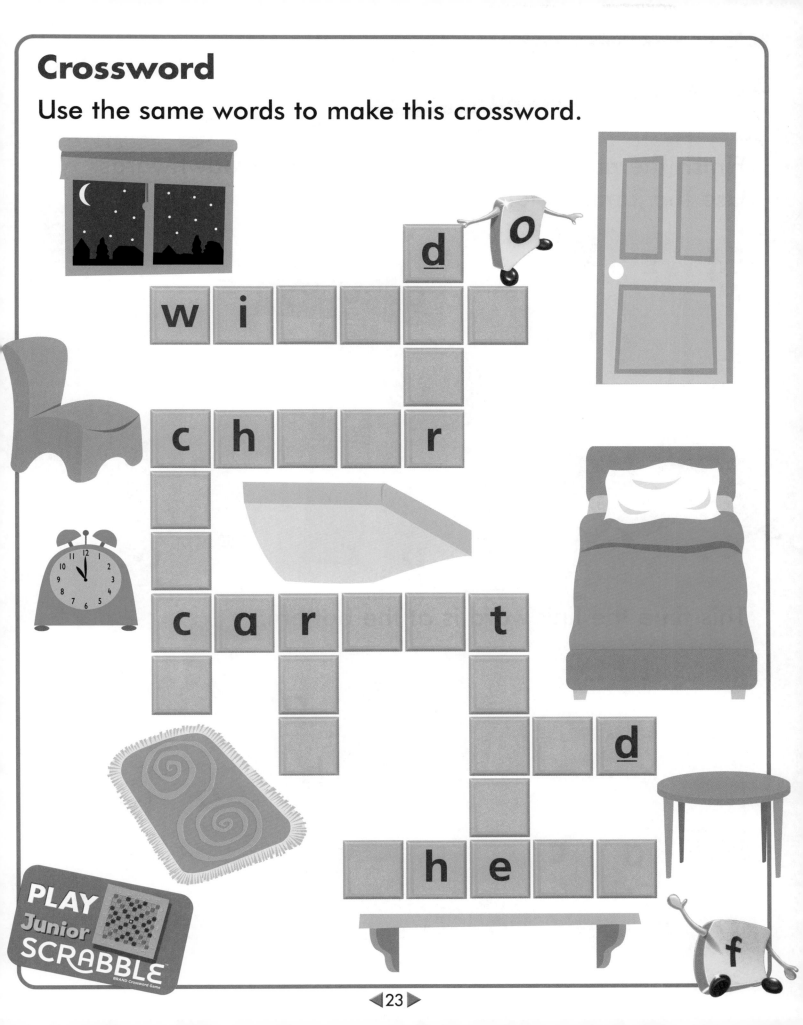

d

w i

o

c h r

c a r t

d

h e

f

LINK WORDS

r o

Finish the puzzles by filling in new words downwards. Use the jumbled letters.

This time the link word is at the bottom.

Now try these, with the link word in the middle.

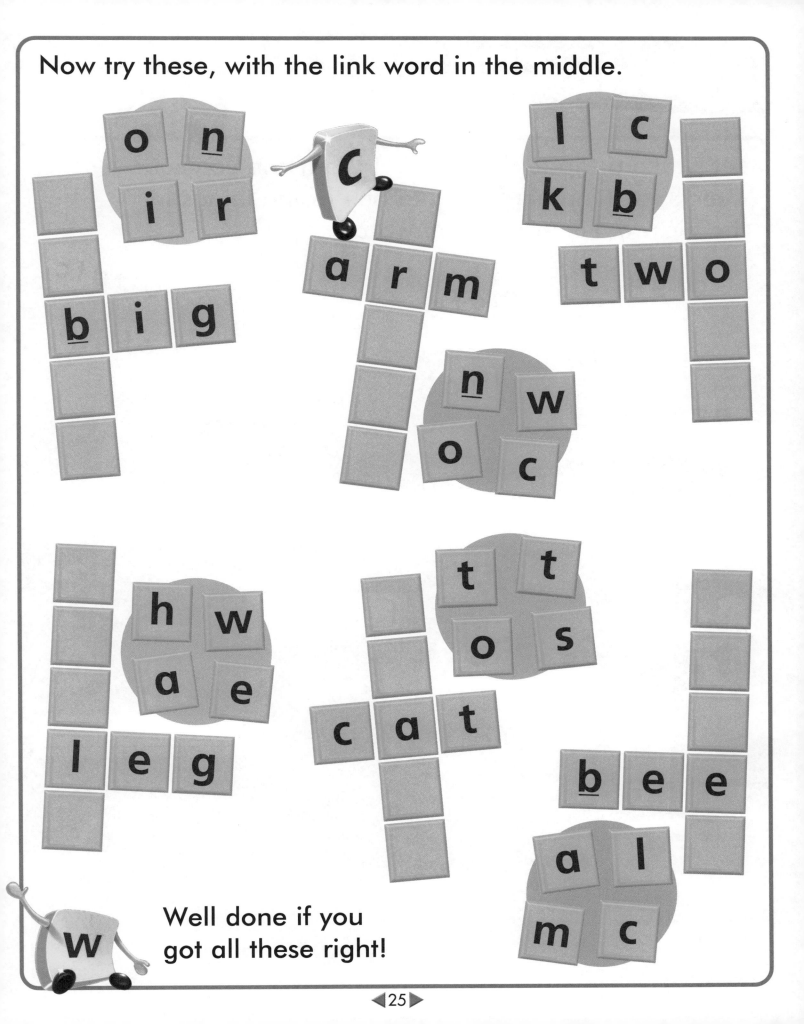

Well done if you
got all these right!

IN THE COUNTRY

Let's take a trip to the country! What can you see?
Match each jumbled word to one of the things in
the picture. Fill in the right word.

ncefe

atge

eltatc

mafr

rcratto

ehsep

eflid

nrab

dgeehs

egees

h_____

f____

b_____

f_____

c_____

t_____

g_____

f_____

s_____

g_____

Use the same words to make this crossword.

CROSSWORD

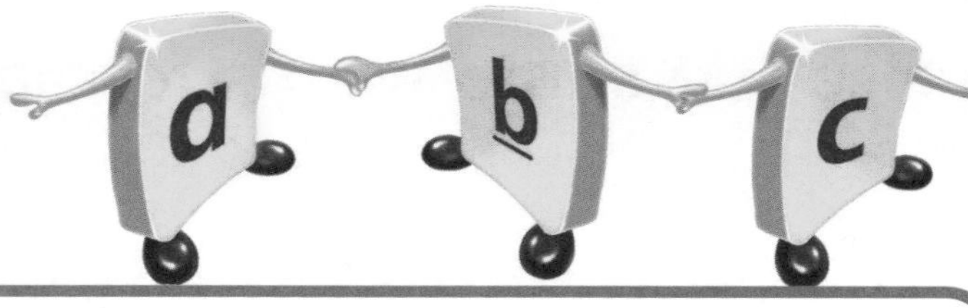

This is a real crossword, with numbers for each clue.
Name each of the picture clues for the Across words.
Write them where the number is, from left to right.
Then do the same for the Down clues.
Write them from top to bottom.

Across

1 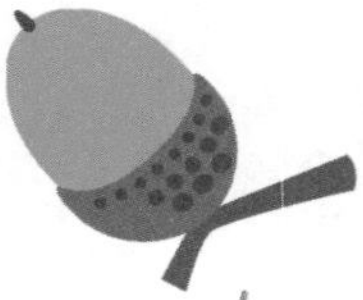

5 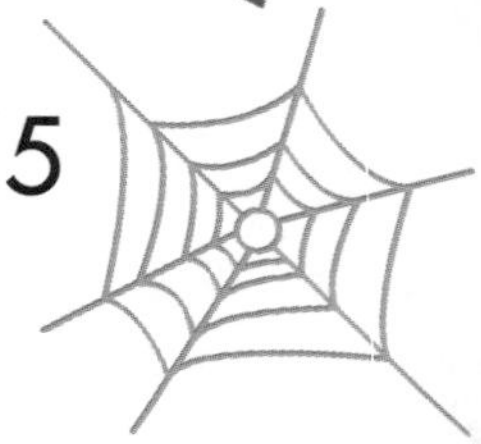

6 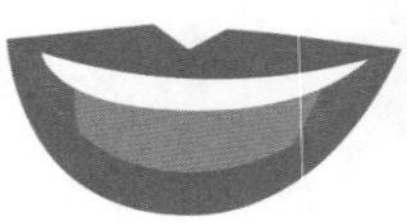

8 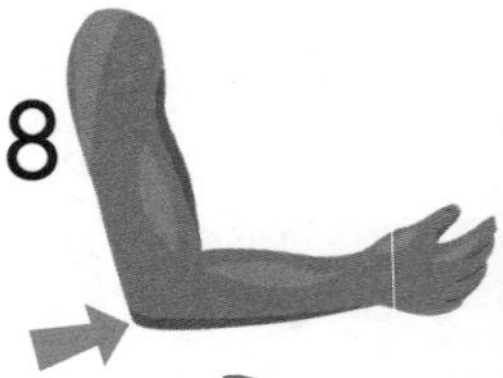

10 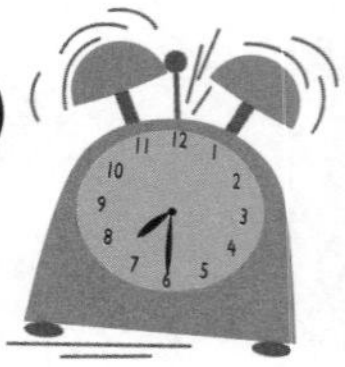

12 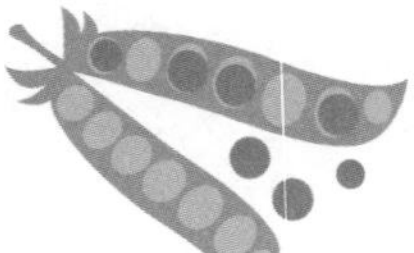

14 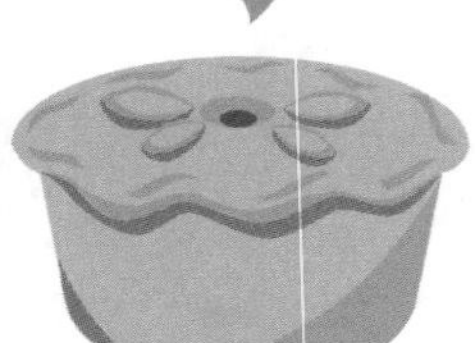

1 a	2 c		3		■	4 z	■
■		■		■	5	e	
6	m		l	7 e	■	r	■
■		■	8			o	9
10 a		11	r	m	■	■	h
	■		■	■	12		a
13 c	a	t	c	h	■	■	
	■		■	■	14 p		e

Down

2 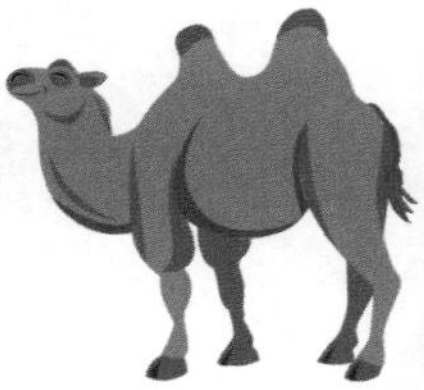

3 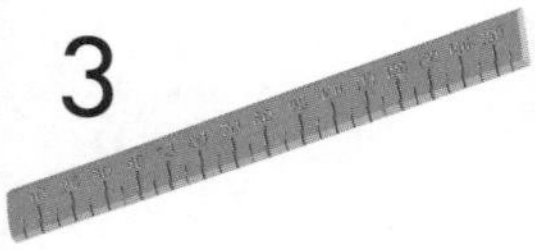

7 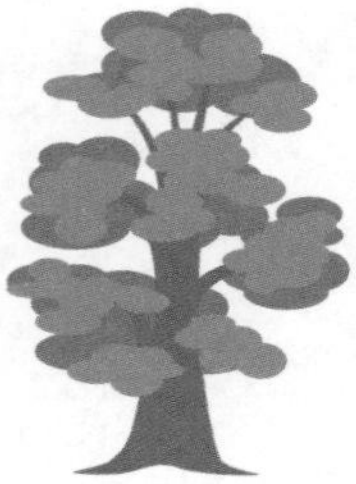

9 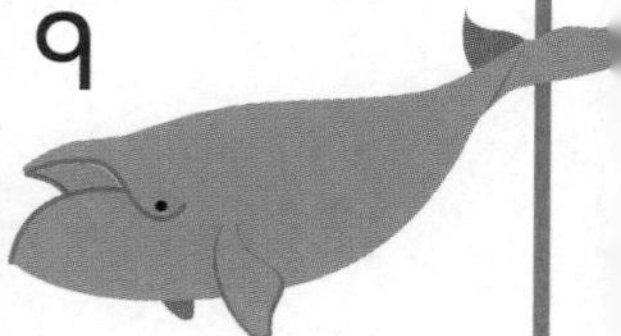

10 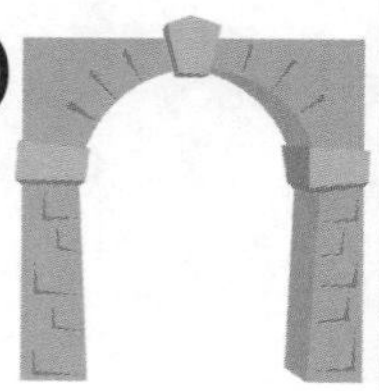

11 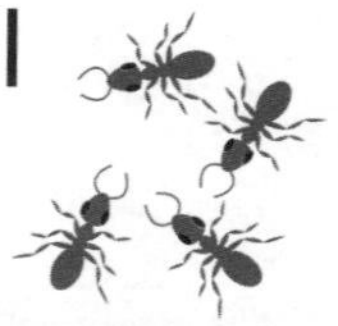

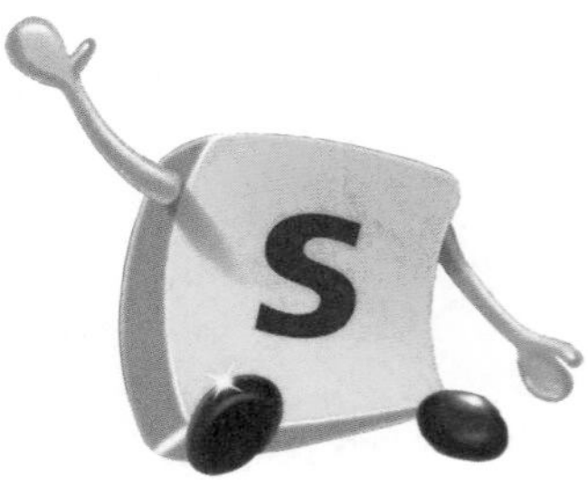

Good food

Sort each set of 5 letters to make something to eat.
Fill in the words in the rows below.

1

2

3

4

5

Now find another food by reading the red squares downwards.

LADDER WORDS

Sort each set of 5 letters to make a real word.

o u h s e

f

e c n e f

h

y l o l h

a t w c h

i c h k c

h r e t e

s r a t s

k r a b e

k u r t n

e g e d h

e a l t b

e d l i s

s l e l b

b

t

t h e i g

Now fill in the same words on this page. Read down the ladder, and you will find 3 birds!

Answers

p2 apple, bee, cat, dog, egg, fox, gate, house, igloo, jam, kite, ladder, mouse, nest, orange, pea, queen, rabbit, star, ten, umbrella, vase, wall, yacht, zebra

p3 d, gj, kp, qt, w; abc, rst, nop, fgh, vwx, xyz

p4 cat, dog, car, van, bus, bed, hat, fox, ten

p5

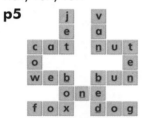

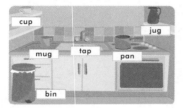

p6 cake, gate, maze, sack, bath, face, path

p7 salt, seal, shed, sail, sink, ship, shoe, swan, star, sock

p8 table, wheel, spoon, clock, plant, brush, train, apple

p9 plane, happy, sheep, spade, crane, cloud, clown, whale

p10 car, van, bus, bike, ship, lorry, train, plane

p11

p12 bed, dog; sit, tea; top, pet; hat, two; cow, web; arm, mug

p13 good, door; help, play; team or tear, mice or rice; post, trap; dream, metal; tooth or toots, hound or sound; table, early; dress, shout

p14 sun, cloud, birds, sky, sails, ship, waves, sea, flag, beach, rock, pool, crab, spade, sand, shell

p15

p16 fox, cup, key, eye, jet, hen, log, ice

p17 book, sock, drum; clock, stamp, mouse

p18 clown, kite, fort, boat, top, robot, crane, tank, bat, doll

p19

p20 cloud

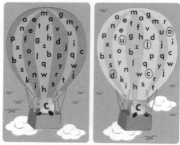

p21 mouse, horse, zebra, tiger, panda; sheep

p22 window, shelf, clock, door, table, bed, rug, chair, carpet

p23

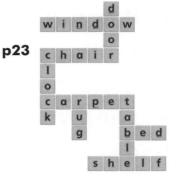

p24 frog, apple, goose; crab, beach, chair

p25 robin, crown, block; whale, toast, camel

p26 barn, hedges, farm, field, cattle, tractor, sheep, gate, fence, geese

p27

p28

p29 bacon, apple, honey, bread, jelly; candy

p30 house, watch, stars, hedge, bells; fence, chick, break, table; holly, three, trunk, slide, eight

p31 robin, duck, eagle